Bram Stoker's
Dracula

Bram Stoker's
Dracula

A Graphic Novel

ILLUSTRATED BY MATT PAGETT

NEW
BURLINGTON
BOOKS

This edition first published in 2016 by
New Burlington Books
The Old Brewery
6 Blundell Street
London N7 9BH
United Kingdom

ISBN 978-0-85762-484-0

Conceived, designed, and produced by
Quid Publishing
Part of the Quarto Group
Level One, Ovest House
58 West Street
Brighton BN1 2RA
United Kingdom
www.quidpublishing.com

Illustrations by Matt Pagett
Script by Lucy York

Printed in China by C&C Offset Printing Co., Ltd.

Contents

Introduction

Dracula was first published in 1897 at the height of the Victorian era. Brimming with fear, terror, and paranormal things going bump in the night and day, it is a classic of the Gothic genre. Critical reaction at the time was mixed, with reviewers calling it "horrid," "sensational," and "powerful", and labeling it as "For Strong Men Only." Numerous reworkings and adaptations have since ensured it remains at the blooded heart of today's popular culture.

The most celebrated work of Anglo-Irish writer Bram Stoker (1847–1912), *Dracula* was written at a time of great social change. Technical advances in warfare, manufacturing, and communication were powering the global reach of Great Britain, where most of the book is set. Change inevitably breeds conflict between the new and the old, and *Dracula* reflects this in various ways. Dr. John Seward's hard science jostles with Professor van Helsing's softer mysticism as the best way to counter the evil they face. The Count himself is the ultimate outsider, a mysterious foreigner representing everything strange, unheard of, and new to the wholly rational band of allies formed against him. Gender roles in Victorian society were also shifting. This is alluded to in the portrayal of Mina Harker, who combines traditional wifely duties with flashes of intellectual brilliance and moral indignation.

Over the years, *Dracula* has also been interpreted as an indictment of empire building, an expression of latent homosexuality, an analysis of contemporary Irish politics, and an examination of the ideas of Sigmund Freud. Its capacity to be pushed and pulled in so many directions illustrates its broad appeal, and supports Stoker's own comment: "I suppose that every book of the kind must contain some lesson, but I prefer that readers should find it out for themselves." All this, of course, pales in comparison with *Dracula's* primary status as a rollicking good adventure.

This particular adaptation focuses on Mina Harker and Dr. van Helsing as the two protagonists. They carry the plot along, personifying some of the book's central themes. The Dutch professor is modeled on Jean-Martin Charcot, a French neurologist who was pursuing similar lines of interest at the time the book was written. Furthermore, from Stoker's description of van Helsing and photographs of Charcot, it would seem that both men sported a rather impressive set of bushy eyebrows.

Dramatis Personae

Dracula

JONATHAN HARKER

COUNT DRACULA

LUCY WESTENRA

JOHN SEWARD

ARTHUR HOLMWOOD

MINA HARKER
(NEE MURRAY)

R. M. RENFIELD

PROFESSOR
VAN HELSING

Chapter One

LEAVING HIS BELOVED FIANCEE MINA BEHIND IN LONDON, THE YOUNG SOLICITOR JONATHAN HARKER TRAVELED BY TRAIN ACROSS THE CONTINENT AND DEEP INTO EASTERN EUROPE. HE HAD BEEN SENT ON BUSINESS TO TRANSYLVANIA, WHERE HE WOULD MEET WITH A CLIENT--A WEALTHY NOBLE BYTHE NAME OF COUNT DRACULA--WHO HAD RECENTLY PURCHASED A LONDON ESTATE. HIS TASK WAS TO GO THROUGH THE RELATED PAPERWORK WITH HIM...

AFTER A JOURNEY BESET BY STRANGE FOOD, QUEER DREAMS, AND LATE-RUNNING TRAINS, HE FINALLY REACHED REMOTE TRANSYLVANIA, WHERE FURTHER INSTRUCTIONS AWAITED HIM AT AN INN...

WELCOME.

THIS MESSAGE WAS LEFT FOR YOU.

Herr Harker

My Friend,

Welcome to the Carpathians. I am anxiously expecting you. The coach will start for Bukovina; a place on it is kept for you. At the Borgo Pass my carriage will await you and will bring you to me. I trust that your journey from London has been a happy one and that you will enjoy your stay in my beautiful land.

Your friend,

Dracula

OH, YOUNG HERR, MUST YOU GO NOW? WHY NOT STAY THE NIGHT? IT IS THE EVE OF ST. GEORGE'S DAY. WHEN THE CLOCK STRIKES MIDNIGHT...

... ALL THE EVIL THINGS IN THE WORLD WILL HAVE FULL SWAY.

THE LOCALS REGARDED HARKER WITH SUPERSTITION AS HE CONTINUED HIS JOURNEY...

... AND OFFERED HIM ITEMS TO WARD OFF EVIL.

AT THE BORGO PASS HE WAS COLLECTED AT THE APPOINTED HOUR BY THE COUNT'S PRIVATE CARRIAGE...

... AND TRAVELED ON INTO DARKEST NIGHT.

WHAT SORT OF GRIM ADVENTURE IS THIS?

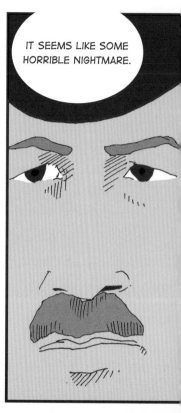

IT SEEMS LIKE SOME HORRIBLE NIGHTMARE.

MIDNIGHT... WHEN ALL EVIL THINGS WILL HOLD SWAY...

OOWWWW

FINALLY, CASTLE DRACULA CAME INTO SIGHT...

UNSETTLED BY THE STRANGE JOURNEY, HARKER APPROACHED THE DOOR...

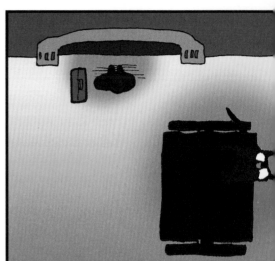

EVENTUALLY THE DOOR CREAKED OPEN...

WELCOME TO MY HOUSE.

I AM DRACULA.

COME FREELY AND LEAVE SOMETHING OF THE HAPPINESS YOU BRING.

LET ME SEE TO YOUR COMFORT MYSELF.

YOU WILL EXCUSE ME IF I DO NOT JOIN YOU. I HAVE DINED ALREADY.

YOU MAY GO ANYWHERE YOU WISH IN THE CASTLE, EXCEPT WHERE THE DOORS ARE LOCKED. OUR WAYS ARE NOT YOUR WAYS, AND THERE SHALL BE TO YOU MANY STRANGE THINGS.

BUT IT IS LATE. YOU MUST BE TIRED.

SLEEP WELL...

... AND DREAM WELL.

DREAM WELL? IN A HOUSE OF LOCKED DOORS AND WARNINGS...?

THE FOLLOWING DAY...

I AM GLAD YOU HAVE FOUND YOUR WAY TO MY LIBRARY.

THROUGH THESE BOOKS I HAVE COME TO KNOW YOUR GREAT ENGLAND.

I LONG TO GO THROUGH THE CROWDED STREETS OF YOUR MIGHTY LONDON.

HERE I AM NOBLE. THE COMMON PEOPLE (COWARDS AND FOOLS!) KNOW ME, AND I AM MASTER.

IN LONDON, HOWEVER, MY SPEAKING WOULD EXPOSE ME AS A STRANGER IN A STRANGE LAND.

BUT YOU SPEAK ENGLISH EXCELLENTLY.

YOUR ESTIMATE IS FLATTERING, YET I FEAR THAT I AM BUT A LITTLE WAY ON THE ROAD I WOULD TRAVEL.

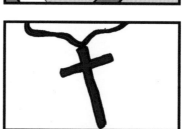

THIS FOUL BAUBLE OF MAN'S VANITY HAS DONE THE MISCHIEF.

AWAY WITH IT!

LATER...

IN NO PLACE SAVE FROM THE WINDOWS IN THE CASTLE WALLS IS THERE AN AVAILABLE EXIT.

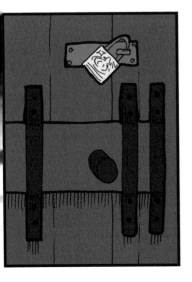

THE CASTLE IS A VERITABLE PRISON...

... AND I AM A PRISONER!

EVERY DAY THE COUNT QUESTIONS ME ABOUT ENGLAND AND LEGAL MATTERS...

...BUT I HAVE SO MANY QUESTIONS OF MY OWN.

WOLVES, CRUCIFIXES, ABSENT SERVANTS--WHAT DOES IT ALL MEAN? YET I MUST KEEP MY KNOWLEDGE AND FEARS TO MYSELF, AND I MUST KEEP MY EYES OPEN.

LATER, IN THE LIBRARY, ANOTHER LONG DISCUSSION OF LEGAL MATTERS WAS DRAWING TO A CLOSE...

... AND SO, THEREFORE, SHOULD I WISH TO SHIP A CONSIGNMENT OF MY GOODS TO ENGLAND...

... I MAY BE AT LIBERTY TO DIRECT SUCH AFFAIRS MYSELF, WITHOUT THE INTERVENTION OF A SOLICITOR?

OF COURSE, AND SUCH IS OFTEN DONE BY MEN OF BUSINESS WHO DO NOT LIKE THE WHOLE OF THEIR AFFAIRS TO BE KNOWN BY ANY ONE PERSON.

GOOD! NOW THEN, YOU MUST WRITE TO YOUR EMPLOYER, MR. HAWKINS, AND SAY THAT YOU SHALL STAY WITH ME FOR A MONTH. I WILL TAKE NO REFUSAL.

I...OF COURSE...I ACCEPT.

I AM TO BE TRAPPED HERE FOR YET ANOTHER MONTH... BUT WHAT ELSE COULD I HAVE DONE?

I PRAY YOU WILL NOT MENTION THINGS OTHER THAN BUSINESS IN YOUR LETTERS...

OH, AND LET ME WARN YOU, MY DEAR YOUNG FRIEND, THAT SHOULD YOU LEAVE THESE ROOMS YOU WILL NOT BY ANY CHANCE GO TO SLEEP IN ANY OTHER PART OF THE CASTLE...

...IT IS OLD, AND HAS MANY MEMORIES...

...AND THERE ARE BAD DREAMS FOR THOSE WHO SLEEP UNWISELY.

SOME DAYS LATER...

CAN ANY DREAM BE MORE TERRIBLE...

...THAN THE UNNATURAL, HORRIBLE NET OF GLOOM AND MYSTERY THAT SEEMS TO CLOSE AROUND ME?

WHAT MANNER OF MAN IS THIS...

... OR WHAT MANNER OF CREATURE IS IT IN THE SEMBLANCE OF MAN?

HAVING WITESSED THE COUNT MAKE HIS EXIT...

... HARKER TOOK THE OPPORTUNITY TO EXPLORE THE CASTLE FURTHER.

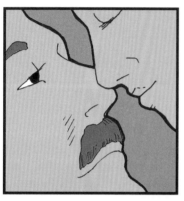

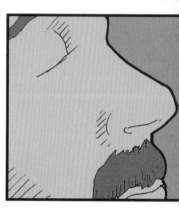
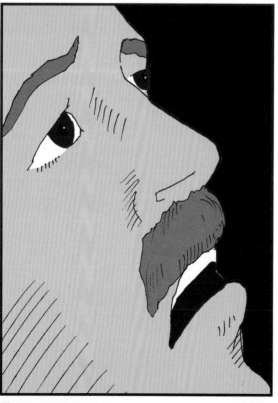

HOW DARE ANY OF YOU TOUCH HIM?

HOW DARE YOU CAST EYES ON HIM WHEN I HAD FORBIDDEN IT? BACK, I TELL YOU ALL! THIS MAN BELONGS TO ME!

YOU YOURSELF NEVER LOVED; YOU NEVER LOVE!

YES, I TOO CAN LOVE.

I PROMISE YOU THAT WHEN I AM DONE WITH HIM, YOU SHALL KISS HIM AT YOUR WILL. NOW GO! I MUST AWAKEN HIM, FOR THERE IS WORK TO BE DONE. TAKE THAT!

TWO WEEKS LATER, GYPSIES ARRIVED AT THE CASTLE WITH SUPPLIES. HARKER SAW HIS CHANCE TO GET A MESSAGE TO THE OUTSIDE WORLD...

Mina Harker,
10 Burlington
Gardens,
London

HELLO!!

PLEASE DELIVER THIS LETTER!

HERE, TAKE IT--AND HERE IS PAYMENT FOR YOU!

BUT THE COUNT GOT THERE FIRST...

I FOUND THESE TWO LETTERS...

... THIS IS NOT SIGNED, SO IT CANNOT MATTER TO US.

UNKNOWINGLY I DID BREAK THE SEAL OF THIS OTHER LETTER, TO YOUR EMPLOYER PETER HAWKINS, TELLING OF YOUR IMMINENT DEPARTURE.

SEAL IT AGAIN. I WILL ENSURE IT IS DELIVERED.

HARKER AWOKE THE FOLLOWING MORNING TO FIND EVERY SCRAP OF PAPER, USEFUL OR OTHERWISE, WAS GONE...

MY NOTES, MY TRAVEL DOCUMENTS, MY LETTER OF CREDIT...

... AND LIKEWISE HIS SUIT AND OVERCOAT.

SOME NEW SCHEME OF VILLAINY!

DISCOVERING HIS OWN DOOR WAS LOCKED...

... HARKER TOOK THE ONLY AVAILABLE EXIT.

DOWN THE WALL...

... ACROSS THE COURTYARD...

... BACK IN THROUGH THE COUNT'S OWN WINDOW...

... AND DOWN TO THE BASEMENT, WHERE HE HAD NEVER VENTURED BEFORE.

WHAT SHALL I DO? HOW CAN I ESCAPE FROM THIS DREADFUL THRALL OF NIGHT AND GLOOM AND FEAR?

AFTER MORE DAYS OF LOCKED DOORS AND UNSPOKEN SCHEMES...

TOMORROW, MY FRIEND, WE MUST PART. MY CARRIAGE SHALL COME FOR YOU IN THE MORNING.

I WOULD WALK WITH PLEASURE. I WANT TO GET AWAY AT ONCE.

VERY WELL, NOT AN HOUR SHALL YOU WAIT IN MY HOUSE AGAINST YOUR WILL.

HARK!

OWW

OWWWWWWW

OWWWWWWW

OWWWWWW OWWWWW

FOR A SECOND TIME...

HIS MOUTH IS FRESHLY SOILED WITH THE BLOOD OF HIS VICTIMS.

TO THINK I HAVE BEEN HELPING TO TRANSFER THIS BEING TO LONDON...

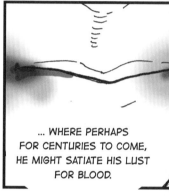

... WHERE PERHAPS FOR CENTURIES TO COME, HE MIGHT SATIATE HIS LUST FOR BLOOD.

THE WORLD MUST BE RID OF SUCH A MONSTER!

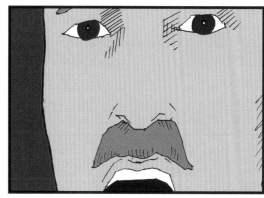

AWAY FROM THIS CURSED SPOT, FROM THIS CURSED LAND. AT LEAST GOD'S MERCY IS BETTER THAN THAT OF THESE MONSTERS, AND THE PRECIPICE IS STEEP AND HIGH. AT ITS FOOT A MAN MAY SLEEP--AS A MAN. GOODBYE ALL!

MINAAAA!!

Chapter Two

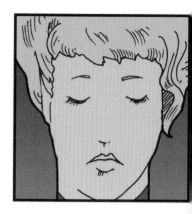

AFTER SUCH EXCITEMENTS, LUCY WAS RELIEVED TO RETREAT TO THE SEASIDE TOWN OF WHITBY, WHERE SHE MET HER DEAR CHILDHOOD FRIEND MINA MURRAY (SOON TO BE HARKER) TO TAKE THE SEA AIR, RELAX, AND OF COURSE FILL HER IN ON ALL THE GOSSIP...

HERE AM I, WHO SHALL BE TWENTY IN SEPTEMBER, AND YET I NEVER HAD A PROPOSAL UNTIL THAT DAY.

JUST FANCY! TWO PROPOSALS IN ONE DAY!

AH, THE NICEST SPOT IN WHITBY. I THINK I WILL OFTEN COME UP HERE TO SIT AND WRITE IN MY JOURNAL.

GOOD DAY, MR. SWALES!

LUCY, MR. SWALES HAS BEEN TELLING ME MUCH ABOUT THE LOCAL LEGENDS.

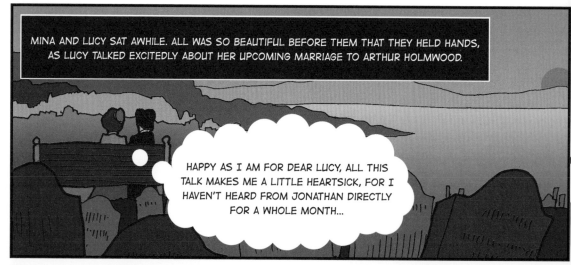

A SINGLE LINE FROM JONATHAN LAST WEEK, VIA DEAR MR. HAWKINS, SAYING THAT HE WAS JUST STARTING FOR HOME FROM CASTLE DRACULA. SINCE THEN, NOTHING.

EVERY NIGHT, THIS SLEEPWALKING... IT MAKES ME UNEASY.

THE NEXT DAY, DARK CLOUDS GATHERED ON THE HORIZON...

BEST BE GETTING HOME, LADIES-- THERE'S A STORM BREWIN'.

THERE'S SOMETHING IN THAT WIND THAT SOUNDS, AND LOOKS, AND TASTES, AND SMELLS LIKE DEATH. IT'S IN THE AIR, I FEEL IT COMIN'.

OUT AT SEA, THE *DEMETER* STRUGGLED ON THE HIGH SEAS. THE SHIP HAD PASSED A TROUBLED VOYAGE FROM VARNA TO ENGLAND...

AS THE WEEKS WENT BY, THE MEN HAD DISAPPEARED ONE BY ONE. THERE WAS TALK OF A STRANGE MAN ROAMING THE DECKS...

CAPTAIN, YET ANOTHER MAN HAS BEEN LOST IN THE NIGHT. THE DARK MAN HAS STRUCK AGAIN!

PAH--NONSENSE! 'TIS NOTHING BUT SUPERSTITION!

WHAT EVIL IS THIS...?

45

THE MORNING AFTER THE STORM, LUCY AND MINA TOOK A WALK DOWN TO THE HARBOR TO SURVEY THE DAMAGE...

THE VILLAGERS HAVE TOLD US OF THE TERRIBLE EVENTS OF LAST NIGHT.

WHAT CARGO ARE THEY UNLOADING FROM THE WRECK?

I KNOW NOT, BUT THERE ARE FIFTY BOXES ALL TOLD, ALL BOUND FOR LONDON.

IT IS AN ILL WIND THAT HAS BROUGHT THIS SHIP TO OUR SHORES. POOR MR. SWALES WAS FOUND DEAD THIS MORNING.

COME, MY DEAR, PERHAPS A BRISK WALK WILL HELP LIFT OUR SPIRITS.

THANK GOD JONATHAN WAS NOT AT SEA LAST NIGHT, BUT, OH-- WHERE IS HE?

THAT NIGHT, MINA AGAIN AWOKE TO FIND LUCY GONE FROM HER BED...

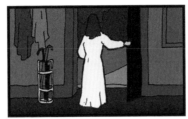

LUCY! LUCY!

WAKE UP, LUCY...

COME, LET'S GET YOU HOME.

NOT A WORD TO ANYONE ABOUT THIS, MINA, I IMPLORE YOU.

AS YOU WISH, MY DEAR.

THE NIGHTS TO COME WERE FRAUGHT WITH UNREST AND MORE SLEEPWALKING...

I FEAR SHE GROWS WEAKER EVERY DAY...

THEN, ONE EVENING AT SUNSET...

Chapter Three

AT HIS LUNATIC ASYLUM NEXT TO THE SPRAWLING CARFAX ESTATE IN THE LONDON SUBURBS, DR. JOHN SEWARD WAS RECORDING HIS THOUGHTS...

SINCE MY REBUFF BY LUCY I HAVE HAD AN EMPTY FEELING. THE ONLY CURE FOR THIS SORT OF THING IS WORK.

ONE OF OUR PATIENTS HAS BEGUN TO FASCINATE ME--R. M. RENFIELD. JUST NOW HIS HOBBY IS CATCHING FLIES... AND EATING THEM.

HE HAS TURNED HIS MIND NOW TO SPIDERS. HE KEEPS FEEDING THEM WITH HIS FLIES...

I WOULD ASK YOU A FAVOR... MAY I HAVE A KITTEN? A NICE, SLEEK KITTEN THAT I CAN PLAY WITH AND FEED--AND FEED!

THERE IS A METHOD IN HIS MADNESS... HE IS WORTHY OF A NEW CLASSIFICATION: A ZOOPHAGOUS MANIAC.

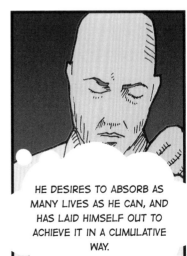

HE DESIRES TO ABSORB AS MANY LIVES AS HE CAN, AND HAS LAID HIMSELF OUT TO ACHIEVE IT IN A CUMULATIVE WAY.

ONE NIGHT THERE WAS A STRANGE AND SUDDEN CHANGE IN REN-FIELD. HE MANAGED TO SLIP PAST THE ATTENDANTS, AND SCALED THE WALL INTO THE NEIGHBORING CARFAX ESTATE...

I AM HERE TO DO YOUR BIDDING, MASTER...

I AM YOUR SLAVE...

...AND YOU WILL REWARD ME...

...FOR I SHALL BE FAITHFUL.

NOW THAT YOU ARE NEAR I AWAIT YOUR COMMANDS.

I SHALL BE PATIENT, MASTER. IT IS COMING-- COMING--COMING!

WHAT A PLEASURE TO SEE YOU, OLD FRIEND!

I'M AFRAID I DO NOT VISIT FOR PLEASURE TODAY. LUCY IS ILL. SHE LOOKS GHASTLY, AND TERRIBLY PALE. SHE IS GETTING WORSE EVERY DAY.

WHEN DID SHE FALL ILL?

THE FOLLOWING WEEK, DR. SEWARD RECEIVED A VISIT FROM ARTHUR HOLMWOOD.

SHE HAS BEEN LIKE THIS SINCE HER RETURN FROM WHITBY. COULD YOU TALK WITH HER TOMORROW? IT WILL BE A PAINFUL TASK FOR YOU, I KNOW, BUT IT IS FOR HER SAKE.

BUT OF COURSE--I WILL DO ALL I CAN.

SHE IS CLEARLY BLOODLESS, BUT I CAN SEE NO SIGNS OF ANEMIA. IT MUST BE SOMETHING MENTAL.

I WILL WRITE TO PROFESSOR VAN HELSING FROM AMSTERDAM, DESCRIBING ALL HER SYMPTOMS AND ASK HIM TO COME AT ONCE! MY OLD FRIEND AND MASTER, AND A REVERED SCIENTIST--HE WILL KNOW WHAT TO DO!

WHEN VAN HELSING RECEIVED DR. SEWARD'S LETTER, HE TRAVELED TO LONDON WITHOUT DELAY...

HAVE YOU SAID ANYTHING TO OUR YOUNG FRIEND, HER LOVER?

NO. I WAITED TILL I HAD SEEN YOU.

BETTER HE NOT KNOW AS YET.

I HAVE MY OWN THOUGHTS AT PRESENT THAT I SHALL UNFOLD TO YOU LATER.

MY GOD, THIS IS DREADFUL! THERE MUST BE A TRANSFUSION OF BLOOD AT ONCE.

JACK, I WAS SO ANXIOUS. I HAD TO KNOW WHAT WAS HAPPENING. IS THIS DR. VAN HELSING?

SIR, YOU HAVE COME IN TIME. AS THE LOVER OF OUR DEAR MISS, YOU ARE TO HELP HER.

MY LIFE IS HERS, AND I WOULD GIVE THE LAST DROP OF BLOOD IN MY BODY FOR HER.

I DO NOT ASK SO MUCH AS THAT!

VERY GOOD.

I MUST GO BACK TO AMSTERDAM TONIGHT. THERE ARE BOOKS AND THINGS THERE I WANT.

KEEP WATCH ALL NIGHT, DO NOT SLEEP. I SHALL BE BACK AS SOON AS POSSIBLE. AND THEN WE MAY BEGIN.

BEGIN WHAT...?

WE SHALL SEE! REMEMBER, SHE IS YOUR CHARGE.

I AM AFRAID TO GO TO SLEEP. IT IS LIKE SOME PRESAGE OF HORROR.

WHAT ON EARTH DO YOU MEAN? I AM HERE WATCHING YOU AND IF I SEE ANY EVIDENCE OF BAD DREAMS I PROMISE TO WAKE YOU AT ONCE.

THE NEXT DAY, LUCY WAS LOOKING MUCH REVIVED...

THERE WILL BE NO SITTING UP TONIGHT FOR YOU. I AM QUITE WELL AGAIN!

THE FOLLOWING DAY...

GOOD MORNING, FRIEND JOHN. TIME TO CHECK ON OUR PATIENT.

MY GOD! WE MUST BEGIN AGAIN, AND I HAVE TO CALL ON YOU YOURSELF THIS TIME, FRIEND JOHN.

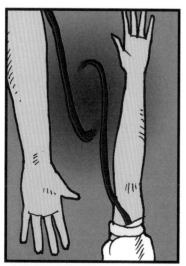

THAT WILL DO.

ALREADY? YOU TOOK A GREAT DEAL MORE FROM ARTHUR.

YES, BUT HE IS HER LOVER, HER FIANCEE. NO WORD TO HIM ABOUT THIS. IT WOULD FRIGHTEN HIM AND MAKE HIM JEALOUS.

TWO DAYS LATER, LUCY HAD RALLIED...

IS THIS A JOKE? THIS IS ONLY COMMON GARLIC.

I NEVER JEST! THERE IS GRIM PURPOSE IN ALL I DO!

IT IS WELL WE HAVE NO SKEPTIC HERE, OR HE WOULD SAY YOU WERE WORKING SOME SPELL TO KEEP OUT AN EVIL SPIRIT.

PERHAPS I AM!

TAKE CARE YOU DO NOT DISTURB IT. AND TONIGHT DO NOT OPEN THE WINDOW OR THE DOOR.

I PROMISE, AND THANK YOU BOTH A THOUSAND TIMES FOR YOUR KINDNESS. I NEVER LIKED GARLIC BEFORE, BUT NOW I FIND PEACE IN ITS SMELL.

TONIGHT I CAN SLEEP IN PEACE.

BUT THE FOLLOWING MORNING...

AH, PROFESSOR, WELCOME. MISS LUCY IS STILL IN BED.

I GOT RID OF THOSE SMELLY FLOWERS AND OPENED THE WINDOW TO LET IN A LITTLE FRESH AIR.

GOD! GOD! WHAT HAVE WE DONE? WHAT HAS SHE DONE? ARE ALL THE POWERS OF THE DEVILS AGAINST US?

TODAY YOU MUST OPERATE. I SHALL PROVIDE. YOU ARE WEAKENED ALREADY.

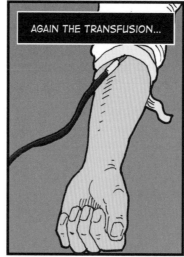

AGAIN THE TRANSFUSION...

... AGAIN SOME RETURN OF COLOR TO THE ASHY CHEEKS.

NOTHING MUST BE REMOVED FROM MISS LUCY'S ROOM WITHOUT MY CONSULTATION. THESE FLOWERS ARE OF MEDICINAL VALUE.

I WILL WATCH OVER HER MYSELF TONIGHT.

WHAT DOES IT ALL MEAN?

HAS MY LONG HABIT OF LIFE AMONGST THE INSANE STARTED TO TELL UPON MY OWN BRAIN?

DR. SEWARD WENT HOME FOR A MUCH-NEEDED EVENING OF RESPITE...

WOLF ESCAPES FROM LONDON ZOO

BUT THE PEACE AND QUIET DIDN'T LAST FOR LONG...

MY GOD, RENFIELD!

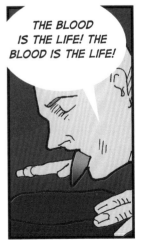

THE BLOOD IS THE LIFE! THE BLOOD IS THE LIFE!

MEANWHILE, LUCY WAS IN GRAVE DANGER TOO. DR. VAN HELSING HAD BEEN CALLED AWAY, LEAVING NO ONE TO WATCH OVER HER...

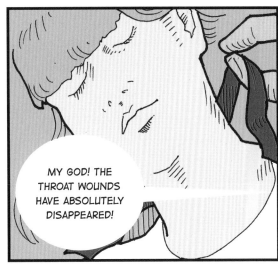

MY GOD! THE THROAT WOUNDS HAVE ABSOLUTELY DISAPPEARED!

SHE IS DYING. IT WILL NOT BE LONG NOW.

OH, ARTHUR, I AM SO GLAD YOU HAVE COME. KISS ME...

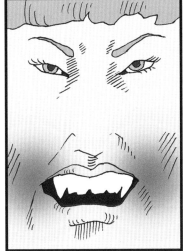

NOT FOR YOUR LIFE. NOT FOR YOUR LIVING SOUL AND HERS!

FRIEND ARTHUR, I KNOW IT MUST BE HARD FOR YOU TO TRUST ME COMPLETELY. BUT I HAVE ANOTHER REQUEST.

I WANT PERMISSION TO READ ALL MISS LUCY'S PAPERS AND LETTERS. IT IS NO IDLE CURIOSITY AND I HAVE AN HONEST MOTIVE. NO WORD SHALL BE LOST.

DR. VAN HELSING, YOU MAY DO WHAT YOU WILL. IN SAYING THIS I AM DOING WHAT MY DEAR ONE WOULD HAVE APPROVED.

WE WILL ALL HAVE TO PASS THROUGH THE BITTER WATER BEFORE WE REACH THE SWEET. BUT WE MUST BE BRAVE OF HEART AND UNSELFISH. DO OUR DUTY, AND ALL WILL BE WELL.

TOMORROW, I WANT YOU TO BRING ME A SET OF POST-MORTEM KNIVES. I WANT TO CUT OFF HER HEAD AND TAKE OUT HER HEART.

AH! YOU A SURGEON AND SO SHOCKED! BUT I MUST NOT FORGET, MY DEAR FRIEND JOHN, THAT YOU LOVED HER.

WHY DO IT AT ALL? THE GIRL IS BARELY DEAD. WHY MUTILATE HER POOR BODY WITHOUT NEED?

THERE ARE THINGS THAT YOU KNOW NOT, BUT THAT YOU SHALL KNOW, AND BLESS ME FOR KNOWING, THOUGH THEY ARE NOT PLEASANT THINGS.

VERY WELL, VAN HELSING. LET US WORK TOGETHER.

THANK YOU, NOW, I STILL HAVE A TELEGRAM TO SEND TO MRS. MINA HARKER. I WISH YOU GOOD NIGHT.

Chapter Four

MEANWHILE, MINA HARKER HAD ARRIVED IN BUDAPEST, WHERE SHE WOULD FINALLY BE REUNITED WITH HER DEAR JONATHAN...

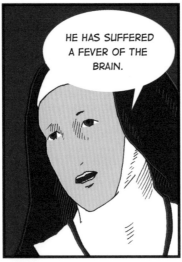

I WILL!

AFTER THE PAIN OF SEPARATION, THEY DECIDED THEY COULD WAIT NO LONGER TO BE UNITED IN THE EYES OF GOD...

YOU KNOW I HAVE HAD A SHOCK, AND WHEN I THINK ON IT I FEEL MAD.

ONCE JONATHAN HAD REGAINED HIS PHYSICAL STRENGTH, THEY PREPARED TO RETURN TO LONDON.

HERE, MY DEAR, IS THE JOURNAL IN WHICH I RECORDED EVERY SORRY DETAIL OF MY TIME IN TRANSYLVANIA. TAKE IT, KEEP IT, READ IT IF YOU WILL, BUT NEVER LET ME KNOW.

I WANT TO TAKE UP MY LIFE NOW, WITH OUR MARRIAGE.

LET THIS JOURNAL REMAIN SO: A VISIBLE SIGN OF OUR UNDYING TRUST.

I WILL NEVER OPEN IT UNLESS IT BE FOR YOUR OWN SAKE, OR THE SAKE OF SOME STERN DUTY. NOW LET US RETURN HOME TO OUR DEAR FRIENDS, MY LOVE.

AFTER THEIR LONG JOURNEY BACK TO LONDON, JONATHAN AND MINA WERE GREETED WITH THE SAD NEWS THAT THEIR EMPLOYER AND GOOD FRIEND, MR. HAWKINS, HAD DIED, LEAVING THEM HIS ESTATE. IT WAS WITH HEAVY HEARTS THAT THEY TOOK UP THEIR INHERITANCE.

WITH DEAR MR. HAWKINS GONE, WHAT SHALL I DO? I DOUBT MY ABILITY TO TAKE UP THE HELM OF THE BUSINESS...

COME, NOW, DO NOT TROUBLE YOURSELF WITH SUCH THOUGHTS. LET US TAKE A WALK TO LIFT OUR SPIRITS.

DO YOU SEE WHO IT IS?

NO, DEAR. WHO IS IT?

MY GOD! IT IS THE MAN HIMSELF!

COME, LET US GO HOME.

SHAKEN BY THE DAY'S EVENTS, THE HARKERS HURRIED HOME, ONLY TO BE GREETED BY YET MORE BAD NEWS...

IT'S DEAR LUCY... SHE... SHE'S DEAD. OH!

GOD HELP US ALL TO BEAR OUR TROUBLES!

THE FOLLOWING DAY, VAN HELSING VISITED THE HARKERS TO FURTHER HIS INVESTIGATIONS.

I HAVE READ YOUR LETTERS TO MISS LUCY. FORGIVE ME, BUT I HAD TO BEGIN SOMEWHERE.

I ASK YOU TO TELL ME ALL THAT YOU REMEMBER, IF YOU HAVE A GOOD MEMORY FOR FACTS.

I WROTE IT ALL DOWN AT THE TIME.

MAY I READ IT?

IF YOU SO WISH.

AH! SHORTHAND! YOU ARE SO VERY CLEVER.

MY LITTLE JOKE, PROFESSOR. HERE, I HAVE A COPY TYPEWRITTEN. READ IT WHILST I ORDER LUNCH.

MADAM MINA! YOUR JOURNAL IS TRULY VALUABLE. THERE IS DARKNESS IN LIFE, BUT YOU ARE ONE OF THE LIGHTS.

TELL ME OF YOUR HUSBAND--IS HIS FEVER GONE?

HE WAS ALMOST RECOVERED, THEN YESTERDAY HE THOUGHT HE SAW SOMEONE WHO REMINDED HIM OF SOMETHING TERRIBLE THAT LED TO HIS BRAIN FEVER. OH...

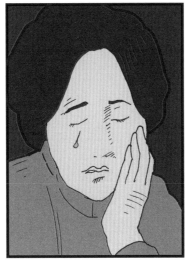

MADAM MINA, YOU HAVE GIVEN ME HOPE. I WILL GLADLY DO ALL I CAN FOR HIM.

WHAT I HAVE TO TELL YOU IS SO QUEER THAT YOU MUST NOT LAUGH AT ME OR AT MY HUSBAND.

IF YOU ONLY KNEW HOW STRANGE IS THE MATTER REGARDING WHICH I AM HERE, IT IS YOU WHO WOULD LAUGH.

HE KEPT A JOURNAL OF HIS TIME IN TRANSYLVANIA. I MADE A PROMISE THAT I WOULD KEEP IT SAFE AND NEVER READ IT.

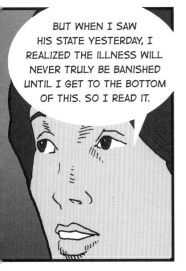

BUT WHEN I SAW HIS STATE YESTERDAY, I REALIZED THE ILLNESS WILL NEVER TRULY BE BANISHED UNTIL I GET TO THE BOTTOM OF THIS. SO I READ IT.

PLEASE, TAKE IT. I DARE NOT SAY ANYTHING OF IT; YOU WILL READ FOR YOURSELF AND JUDGE.

I HAVE READ YOUR PAPERS AND DIARIES. STRANGE AND TERRIBLE AS THEIR STORIES ARE, THEY ARE TRUE, NO DOUBT.

YOUR BELIEF LIFTS MY CLOUD OF ILLNESS, DEAR PROFESSOR.

AND YET WHAT AN AWFUL THING IF THAT MAN, THAT MONSTER, BE REALLY IN LONDON!

IT WAS THE DOUBT TO THE REALITY OF THE WHOLE THING THAT KNOCKED ME OVER. I FELT IMPOTENT.

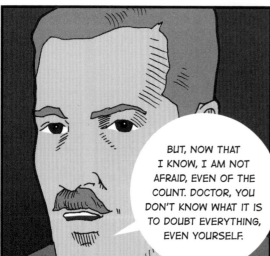

BUT, NOW THAT I KNOW, I AM NOT AFRAID, EVEN OF THE COUNT. DOCTOR, YOU DON'T KNOW WHAT IT IS TO DOUBT EVERYTHING, EVEN YOURSELF.

YOU MAY BE SURPRISED, FRIEND JONATHAN. BUT NOW, CAN YOU TELL ME WHAT WENT BEFORE YOUR GOING TO TRANSYLVANIA?

IT IS ALL WRITTEN HERE. YOU MAY TAKE THESE TO READ AT YOUR LEISURE.

THAT AFTERNOON VAN HELSING WENT TO DISCUSS HIS FINDINGS WITH DR. SEWARD...

I SAY, LISTEN TO THIS:

CHILDREN IN HAMPSTEAD... GOING MISSING FROM THE HEATH... SAYING THAT THEY HAVE BEEN WITH A "BEAUTIFUL LADY"... ALL TURN UP EVENTUALLY...

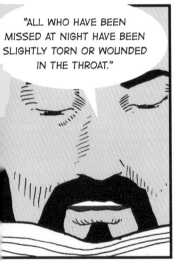

"ALL WHO HAVE BEEN MISSED AT NIGHT HAVE BEEN SLIGHTLY TORN OR WOUNDED IN THE THROAT."

LIKE POOR LUCY'S THROAT.

AND WHAT DO YOU MAKE OF IT?

SIMPLY THAT THERE IS SOME COMMON CAUSE.

HAVE YOU NO SUSPICION AS TO WHAT POOR LUCY DIED OF?

OF NERVOUS PROSTRATION FOLLOWING ON GREAT LOSS OR WASTE OF BLOOD.

YOU ARE A CLEVER MAN, FRIEND JOHN, BUT YOU ARE TOO PREJUDICED.

AS NIGHT FELL, THE TWO MEN MADE THEIR WAY TO THE WESTENRA TOMB.

USING A DUPLICATE KEY, VAN HELSING ENTERED FIRST AND PRIED OPEN THE LID OF LUCY'S COFFIN.

PROFESSOR, PLEASE STOP.

YOU SHALL SEE.

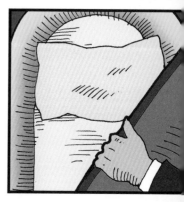

PERHAPS A BODY-SNATCHER? SOME OF THE UNDERTAKER'S PEOPLE?

AH, WELL, WE MUST HAVE MORE PROOF. COME WITH ME.

THEY THEN STARTED A LONELY VIGIL AT EITHER SIDE OF THE CHURCHYARD.

SUDDENLY, IN THE DEPTHS OF THE NIGHT...

ARE YOU SATISFIED NOW?

NO. WHO BROUGHT THE CHILD HERE? AND IS HE WOUNDED?

BY THE LIGHT OF A MATCH THEY EXAMINED THE CHILD'S NECK...

NO, WE WERE JUST IN TIME.

LEAVING THE CHILD IN THE PATH OF A PATROLLING POLICEMAN, THE MEN RETURNED HOME.

THE PAIR RETURNED TO THE GRAVEYARD IN BROAD DAYLIGHT...

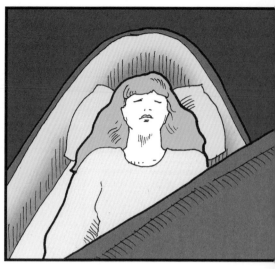

SEE, THEY ARE EVEN SHARPER THAN BEFORE. WITH THESE, CHILDREN CAN BE BITTEN. ARE YOU OF BELIEF NOW, FRIEND JOHN?

SHE MAY HAVE BEEN PLACED HERE SINCE LAST NIGHT.

AND YET SHE HAS BEEN DEAD ONE WEEK. MOST PEOPLE WOULD NOT LOOK SO WELL-PRESERVED.

SHE WAS BITTEN BY A VAMPIRE WHILE SLEEPWALKING, IN A TRANCE.

SHE--IT--IS THUS UNDEAD.

HER HEAD MUST BE SEVERED, HER MOUTH FILLED WITH GARLIC AND A STAKE DRIVEN THROUGH HER BODY. AND IT MAY BE BEST DONE BY ARTHUR.

THE PROSPECT OF SUCH MUTILATION APPALLS ME.

AND YET, THIS BEING, THIS UNDEAD, BEGINS TO ENCOURAGE A DEEP LOATHING WITHIN ME. IS IT POSSIBLE THAT LOVE IS ALL SUBJECTIVE OR ALL OBJECTIVE?

ARTHUR WILL NEED TO CROSS AN OCEAN OF DISBELIEF TO TRUST ME. LET US LEAVE HERE NOW, AND ALL MEET TOMORROW.

THE NEXT DAY, AT THE BERKELEY HOTEL...

AND WHAT IS THAT?

I WANT YOUR PERMISSION TO DO WHAT I THINK GOOD THIS NIGHT.

I WANT YOU TO COME WITH ME TO THE CHURCHYARD AT KINGSTEAD.

WHERE POOR LUCY IS BURIED?

TO ENTER THE TOMB...

IS THIS SOME MONSTROUS JOKE?

... TO OPEN THE COFFIN...

THIS IS TOO MUCH!

81

IT WAS APPROACHING MIDNIGHT WHEN THEY ARRIVED AT THE GRAVEYARD.

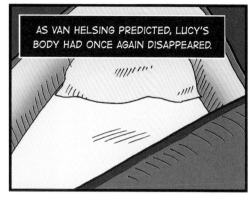

AS VAN HELSING PREDICTED, LUCY'S BODY HAD ONCE AGAIN DISAPPEARED.

WHAT ARE YOU DOING?

I AM SEALING THE TOMB, SO THAT THE UNDEAD MAY NOT ENTER.

THIS IS THE HOLY HOST, WHICH I HAVE BROUGHT WITH ME FROM AMSTERDAM.

MY LUCY!

THE VERY NEXT DAY THE THREE FRIENDS SOLEMNLY RETURNED TO COMPLETE THEIR TASK.

THE UNDEAD CANNOT DIE.

THEY MUST GO ON, AGE AFTER AGE, ADDING NEW VICTIMS. FOR ALL THAT DIE FROM THE PREYING OF THE UNDEAD BECOME THEMSELVES UNDEAD.

ARTHUR, THIS FATE WOULD HAVE BEFALLEN YOU HAD YOU ACCEPTED LUCY'S KISS LAST NIGHT.

BUT THOSE CHILDREN ON WHICH SHE HAS FED CAN YET BE SAVED--IF SHE DIE IN TRUTH, THEIR WOUNDS WILL HEAL AND THEY CAN RETURN TO THEIR INNOCENT GAMES.

MY FRIEND, IT WILL BE A BLESSED HAND FOR HER THAT WILL STRIKE THE BLOW THAT SETS HER FREE.

TELL ME WHAT I AM TO DO.

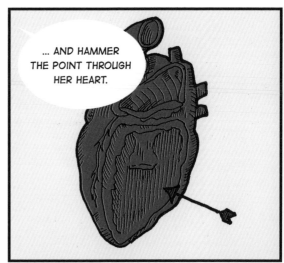

MY CHILD, YOU MAY KISS HER NOW. FOR SHE IS NOT A GRINNING DEVIL ANY MORE.

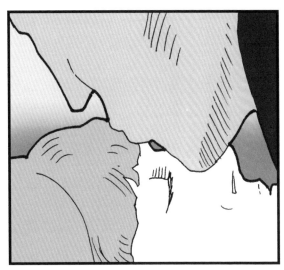

AND NOW, TO FINISH OUR WORK, WE MUST SAW OFF THE HEAD AND STUFF THE MOUTH WITH GARLIC.

ONE STEP OF OUR WORK IS DONE. BUT THERE REMAINS A SECOND, GREATER TASK: TO FIND OUT THE AUTHOR OF ALL THIS SORROW AND TO STAMP HIM OUT!

Chapter Five

WITH VAN HELSING RETURNED FROM HIS RESEARCH TRIP, THE WHOLE PARTY GATHERED TO DISCUSS THE GRIM TASK AHEAD OF THEM...

I THINK GOOD THAT I TELL YOU SOMETHING OF THE KIND OF ENEMY WE FACE.

THERE ARE SUCH BEINGS AS VAMPIRES. SOME OF US HAVE EVIDENCE THAT THEY EXIST.

THIS VAMPIRE WHICH IS AMONG US IS AS STRONG AS TWENTY MEN.

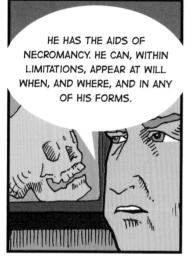

HE HAS THE AIDS OF NECROMANCY. HE CAN, WITHIN LIMITATIONS, APPEAR AT WILL WHEN, AND WHERE, AND IN ANY OF HIS FORMS.

HE CAN DIRECT THE ELEMENTS: THE STORM, THE FOG, THE THUNDER.

HE CAN COMMAND ALL MEANER THINGS: THE RAT, THE BAT, THE WOLF.

HE CAN GROW AND BECOME SMALL. HE CAN AT TIMES VANISH AND BECOME UNKNOWN.

HOW THEN ARE WE TO DESTROY HIM?

MY FRIENDS, IT IS A TERRIBLE TASK THAT WE UNDERTAKE. BUT WE MUST NOT FAIL, FOR IF WE DO, HE WILL SURELY WIN.

WHO IS WITH ME?

93

95

YOU KNOW THIS PLACE, JONATHAN. YOU HAVE SEEN THE MAPS. WHICH IS THE WAY TO THE CHAPEL?

THIS IS THE SPOT.

EVERY BREATH EXHALED BY THAT MONSTER SEEMS TO HAVE CLUNG TO THE PLACE AND INTENSIFIED ITS LOATHSOMENESS!

... 27, 28, 29. WHERE, THEN, ARE THE OTHER 21 BOXES?

I THOUGHT I SAW A FACE IN THE SHADOWS.

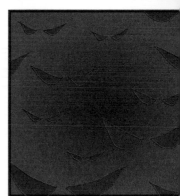

IT IS STRANGE TO ME TO BE KEPT IN THE DARK AS I AM.

AFTER HAVING JONATHAN'S FULL CONFIDENCE FOR SO MANY YEARS, IT PAINS ME TO SEE HIM MANIFESTLY AVOID CERTAIN MATTERS. TO THINK THAT HE KEEPS ANYTHING FROM ME!

OH, SUCH ANXIETY-- EVERYTHING SEEMS LIKE A HORRIBLE TRAGEDY, WITH FATE PRESSING ON TO SOME DESTINED END.

IF I HADN'T GONE TO WHITBY, PERHAPS POOR DEAR LUCY WOULD BE WITH US NOW.

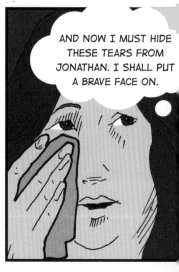

AND NOW I MUST HIDE THESE TEARS FROM JONATHAN. I SHALL PUT A BRAVE FACE ON.

I SUPPOSE IT IS ONE OF THE LESSONS THAT WE WOMEN HAVE TO LEARN.

WHAT SOUND IS THAT?

POOR RENFIELD, HOW HE SUFFERS.

THEN, A DEATHLY SILENCE...

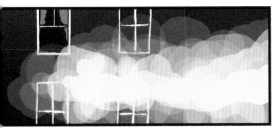

THOSE RED EYES... JUST THE SAME AS THE ONES LUCY SPOKE OF...

Chapter Six

WOULD YOU LIKE SOME SUGAR TO GET YOUR FLIES ROUND AGAIN? OR SPIDERS?

BLOW FLIES, AND BLOW SPIDERS! THERE ISN'T ANYTHING IN THEM TO EAT OR DRI--

OR DRINK?

HE WILL NOT MENTION "DRINKING"...

... AND HE FEARS THE THOUGHT OF BEING BURDENED WITH THE "SOUL" OF ANYTHING...

HE HAS THE ASSURANCE OF SOME KIND THAT HE WILL ACQUIRE SOME HIGHER LIFE.

THEN IT IS A HUMAN LIFE HE LOOKS TO! AND THE ASSURANCE?

MERCIFUL GOD! THE COUNT HAS BEEN TO HIM, AND THERE IS SOME NEW SCHEME OF TERROR AFOOT! I MUST TELL VAN HELSING...

AH, DR. SEWARD. HARKER IS JUST UPDATING US ON HIS INVESTIGATIONS.

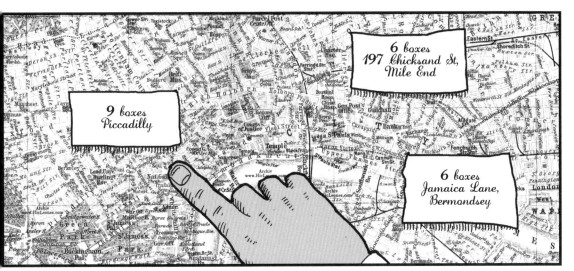

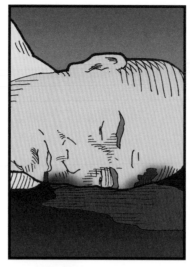

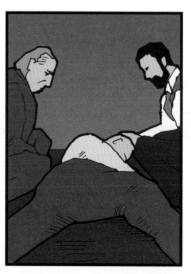

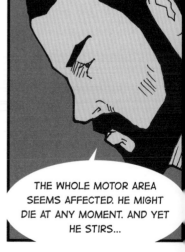

MOVING ANYONE IN SUCH A CONDITION IS OF COURSE TANTAMOUNT TO TORTURE BUT HIS WORDS MAY BE WORTH MANY LIVES. IF WE COULD AFFORD HIM SOME SMALL COMFORT.

I HAVE HAD A TERRIBLE DREAM!

AND WHAT OF IT, MR. RENFIELD?

I MUST NOT DECEIVE MYSELF; IT WAS NO DREAM, BUT ALL A GRIM REALITY.

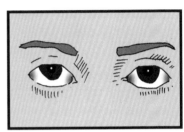

QUICK, THE BRANDY!

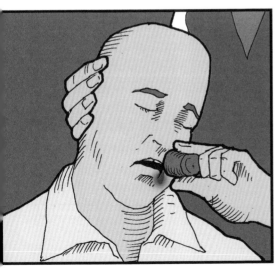

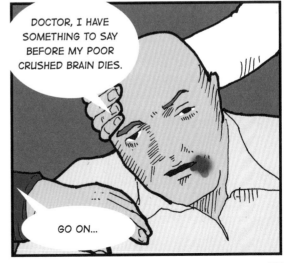

DOCTOR, I HAVE SOMETHING TO SAY BEFORE MY POOR CRUSHED BRAIN DIES.

GO ON...

THE NIGHT WHEN I IMPLORED YOU TO LET ME GO....

... AFTER YOU LEFT ME, HE CAME UP TO THE WINDOW IN A MIST, AS I HAD SEEN HIM BEFORE.

BUT THEN HE WAS SOLID, AND HIS EYES FIERCE.

I WOULDN'T ASK HIM TO COME IN AT FIRST, THOUGH I KNEW HE WANTED TO--AS HE HAD WANTED ALL ALONG.

HE BEGAN PROMISING ME THINGS. HE WHISPERED TO ME...

"I WILL SEND YOU RATS, HUNDREDS, THOUSANDS, MILLIONS OF THEM...

... AND CATS TO EAT THEM, AND DOGS, TOO.

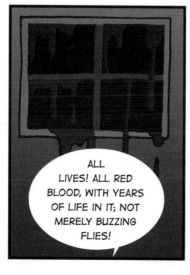

ALL LIVES! ALL RED BLOOD, WITH YEARS OF LIFE IN IT; NOT MERELY BUZZING FLIES!

ALL THESE LIVES WILL I GIVE YOU, AND MANY MORE, GREATER, THROUGH COUNTLESS AGES, IF YOU WILL FALL DOWN AND WORSHIP ME!"

I FOUND MYSELF OPENING THE WINDOW AND SAYING TO HIM, "COME IN, LORD AND MASTER!"

GOOD GOD...

SSH! LET HIM GO ON!

HE DIDN'T STAY LONG. ALL DAY TODAY I WAITED TO HEAR FROM HIM, BUT HE SENT ME NOTHING, NOT EVEN A FLY. I WAS MAD AT HIM.

THIS EVENING I WAS READY FOR HIM. I GRABBED THE MIST AS IT CAME IN. BUT HE SLIPPED THROUGH, AND RAISED ME UP AND FLUNG ME DOWN...

OH, MADAM MINA, WHAT HAVE I DONE!

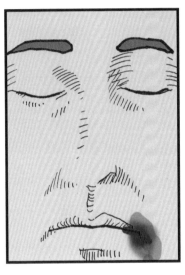

WE KNOW THE COUNT IS HERE. LET US BE ARMED.

COME, ARTHUR, NOT A MOMENT TO LOSE!

INDEED, THERE WASN'T A MOMENT TO LOSE. AT THAT VERY MOMENT, THE COUNT HAD INSINUATED HIMSELF INTO THE HARKERS' BEDROOM...

SILENCE! IF YOU MAKE A SOUND I SHALL TAKE YOUR DEAR SLEEPING BEAUTY OVER THERE AND DASH HIS BRAINS OUT BEFORE YOUR VERY EYES.

FIRST, A LITTLE REFRESHMENT TO REWARD MY EXERTIONS.

YOU MAY AS WELL BE QUIET; IT IS NOT THE FIRST TIME THAT YOUR VEINS HAVE APPEASED MY THIRST!

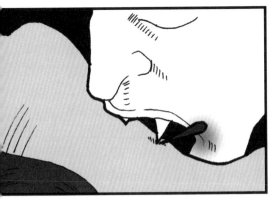

AND SO YOU, LIKE THE OTHERS, WOULD PLAY YOUR BRAINS AGAINST MINE.

YOU WOULD HELP THESE MEN TO HUNT ME AND FRUSTRATE ME IN MY DESIGNS! BUT WHILST THEY PLAY THEIR WITS AGAINST ME, I COUNTERMINE THEM.

AND YOU, THEIR BEST BELOVED ONE, ARE NOW TO ME, FLESH OF MY FLESH; BLOOD OF MY BLOOD; MY BOUNTIFUL WINE-PRESS FOR A WHILE; AND SHALL BE LATER ON MY COMPANION AND MY HELPER.

YOU WILL COME TO MY CALL TO DO MY BIDDING. AND TO THAT END...

... THIS!

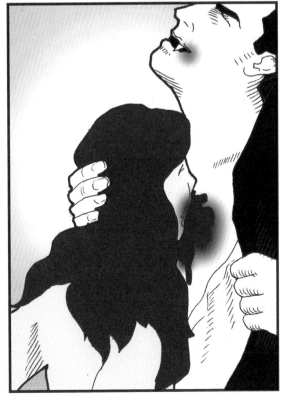

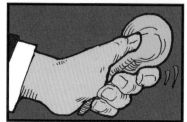

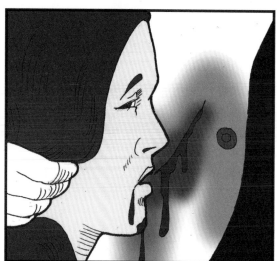

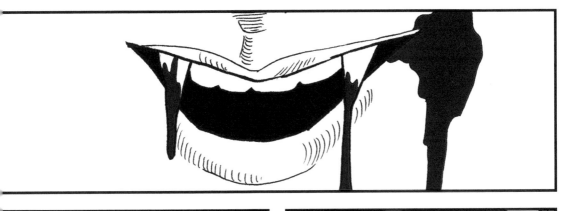

BLAST THE DEVIL!
I WILL FIND HIM!

113

IN GOD'S NAME, WHAT HAS HAPPENED?

WHAT DOES THIS BLOOD MEAN?

OH, DO SOMETHING TO SAVE HER. GUARD HER WHILE I LOOK FOR HIM!

NO, JONATHAN, YOU MUST NOT LEAVE ME. I HAVE SUFFERED ENOUGH TONIGHT.

DO NOT FEAR, MY DEAR. WE ARE HERE; AND WHILST THIS IS CLOSE TO YOU NO FOUL THING CAN APPROACH.

UNCLEAN! I MUSTN'T TOUCH OR KISS YOU ANY MORE.

NONSENSE, MINA. I WILL NOT HAVE SUCH TALK!

WHAT NEWS?

114

I COULD NOT SEE HIM ANYWHERE IN THE PASSAGE, OR THE STUDY, BUT HE HAD BEEN THERE-- THE JOURNALS ARE ALL BURNED!

THANK GOD WE MADE COPIES!

AND MORE DISTRESS: POOR RENFIELD IS DEAD.

GOD'S WILL BE DONE.

I SAW A BAT RISE FROM THE WINDOW AND FLAP AWAY WESTWARD.

HE EVIDENTLY SOUGHT SOME OTHER LAIR. HE WILL NOT BE BACK TONIGHT.

OF THIS I AM SURE: THE SUN RISES TODAY ON NO MORE MISERABLE HOUSE IN ALL THE GREAT ROUND OF ITS DAILY COURSE.

WEARY FROM THE NIGHT'S EVENTS, THE GROUP MET AT BREAKFAST TO FORMULATE A PLAN OF ACTION...

THERE MUST BE NO MORE CONCEALMENT. WE HAVE HAD TOO MUCH OF IT ALREADY.

AND BESIDES, NOTHING CAN GIVE ME MORE PAIN THAN WHAT I HAVE ALREADY ENDURED.

BUT DEAR MADAM MINA, DO YOU NOT FEAR THAT YOU MAY HARM OTHERS?

AH, NO, FOR MY MIND IS MADE UP! IF I FIND IN MYSELF A SIGN OF HARM TO ANY I LOVE, I SHALL DIE!

YOU WOULD NOT KILL YOURSELF?

I WOULD, IF THERE WAS NO ONE WHO LOVED ME WHO WOULD DO IT ON MY BEHALF.

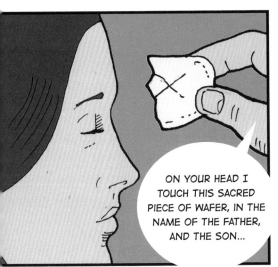

ON YOUR HEAD I TOUCH THIS SACRED PIECE OF WAFER, IN THE NAME OF THE FATHER, AND THE SON...

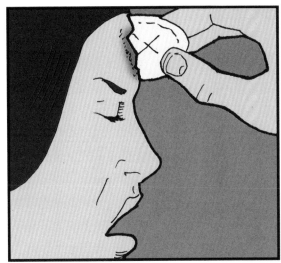

IT BURNS! UNCLEAN! I AM UNCLEAN! EVEN THE ALMIGHTY SHUNS MY POLLUTED FLESH!

DEAR MINA, WE PLEDGE OURSELVES TO RID THE EARTH OF THE MONSTER.

WHEN HE IS GONE, GOD WILL SURELY WIPE AWAY THAT MARK AND LEAVE YOUR FOREHEAD PURE AS THE HEART WE KNOW.

WE WILL NOT FAIL YOU, MINA!

Chapter Seven

THE FOUR FRIENDS ENTERED CARFAX AND BEGAN THEIR TASK OF STERILIZING THE BOXES OF EARTH...

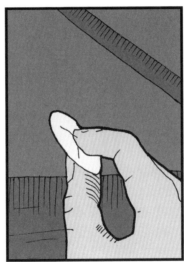

AND NOW, TO PICCADILLY TO CONTINUE OUR WORK.

AT PICCADILLY, THEY HIRED A LOCKSMITH TO GAIN ENTRY TO THE HOUSE.

HE HAD A MIGHTY BRAIN, AND LEARNING BEYOND COMPARE.

HE IS EXPERIMENTING HERE, AND DOING IT WELL.

A TELEGRAM! FROM MINA...

"'LOOK OUT FOR D. HE HAS JUST NOW, 12:45, COME FROM CARFAX AND HASTENED TOWARD THE SOUTH."

NOW, GOD BE THANKED, WE SHALL SOON MEET!

COME QUICKLY INSIDE AND TELL US YOUR NEWS.

IT IS ALL RIGHT. WE FOUND BOTH PLACES; SIX BOXES IN EACH, AND DESTROYED THEM ALL.

DESTROYED?

THERE IS NOTHING TO DO NOW BUT WAIT HERE. THOUGH IF HE DOESN'T APPEAR BY FIVE O'CLOCK WE MUST START OFF. IT WON'T DO TO LEAVE MRS. HARKER ALONE AFTER SUNSET.

BUT THEN...

YOU SHALL BE SORRY YET, EACH ONE OF YOU!

YOU THINK YOU HAVE LEFT ME WITHOUT A PLACE TO REST; BUT I HAVE MORE. MY REVENGE HAS JUST BEGUN!

YOUR GIRLS THAT YOU ALL LOVE ARE MINE ALREADY; AND THROUGH THEM YOU AND OTHERS SHALL YET BE MINE--MY CREATURES, TO DO MY BIDDING.

BAH!

WE HAVE LEARNED SOMETHING.

NOTWITHSTANDING HIS BRAVE WORDS, HE FEARS US.

LET US GO BACK TO MADAM MINA. ALL WE CAN DO HERE IS NOW DONE.

WITH THE COMING OF NIGHT, THE MEN RETURNED TO MINA'S SIDE AND SET UP A WATCH, DETERMINED TO KEEP HER SAFE...

GO, CALL THE PROFESSOR. I WANT TO SEE HIM AT ONCE.

I HAVE AN IDEA. HE MUST HYPNOTIZE ME BEFOR THE DAWN.

IS EVERYTHING WELL? I HEARD VOICES.

SEND FOR VAN HELSING.

OH, MY DEAR MADAM MINA, THIS IS INDEED A CHANGE. YOU SEEM YOUR OLD SELF!

I WANT YOU TO HYPNOTIZE ME BEFORE DAWN. FOR I FEEL THEN I CAN SPEAK FREELY.

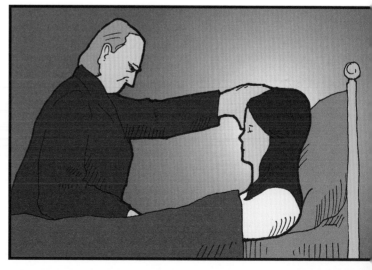

THEY HASTENED TO LLOYD'S DOCKS, WHERE NOTE WAS KEPT OF ALL SHIPS THAT SAILED, HOWEVER SMALL.

TO THE BLACK SEA, YOU SAY?

THE ONLY SHIP TRAVELING THERE IS THE *CZARINA CATHERINE*, SAILING TO VARNA, FROM WHERE SHE WILL TRAVEL ON UP THE DANUBE.

THANK YOU, GOOD SIR.

WELL, THANK *YOU*, GOOD SIR! SHE SET SAIL YESTERDAY SHE DID, SIR.

AND DID YOU SEE ANY, ER, UNUSUAL PASSENGERS?

WELL, NOW THAT YOU MENTION IT, SIR...

... A TALL, THIN MAN WITH EYES A-BURNING, DRESSED ALL IN BLACK AND A STRAW HAT THAT DIDN'T MATCH.

HE ASKED THE CAPTAIN TO STALL THE SHIP WHILE HE FETCHED A BOX HE WANTED TO LOAD. CAPTAIN WASN'T HAVING ANY OF THAT.

BUT A MIST CAME STEALING UP THE RIVER AND DELAYED HIM ANYWAYS.

THEN IT IS AS WE SUSPECTED. BUT TO SAIL A SHIP TAKES TIME.

WE CAN MAKE BETTER TIME OVERLAND AND MEET HIM THERE.

LET US GO AND PREPARE.

BACK AT DR. SEWARD'S...

FRIEND JOHN, MADAM MINA IS CHANGING. I CAN SEE THE CHARACTERISTICS OF THE VAMPIRE COMING IN HER FACE.

HER TEETH ARE SHARPER, HER EYES SOMETIMES HARD. BUT MORE WORRYING, SHE IS OFTEN SILENT. NOW MY FEAR IS THIS...

... IF SHE CAN TELL WHAT THE COUNT SEES AND HEARS, COULD HE, BY THE SAME, COMPEL HER MIND TO DISCLOSE TO HIM THAT WHICH SHE KNOWS?

THEN WE MUST KEEP OUR INTENTIONS HIDDEN FROM MINA.

OH, THIS IS A PAINFUL TASK!

JONATHAN LOOKED ON AS HIS DEAR MINA SLEPT, SEARCHING HER FACE FOR ANY SIGN OF THE CHANGES DESCRIBED BY VAN HELSING.

JONATHAN, I WANT YOU TO PROMISE ME SOMETHING ON YOUR WORD.

NEVER TELL ME ANYTHING OF YOUR PLANS FOR THE CAMPAIGN AGAINST THE COUNT.

Chapter Eight

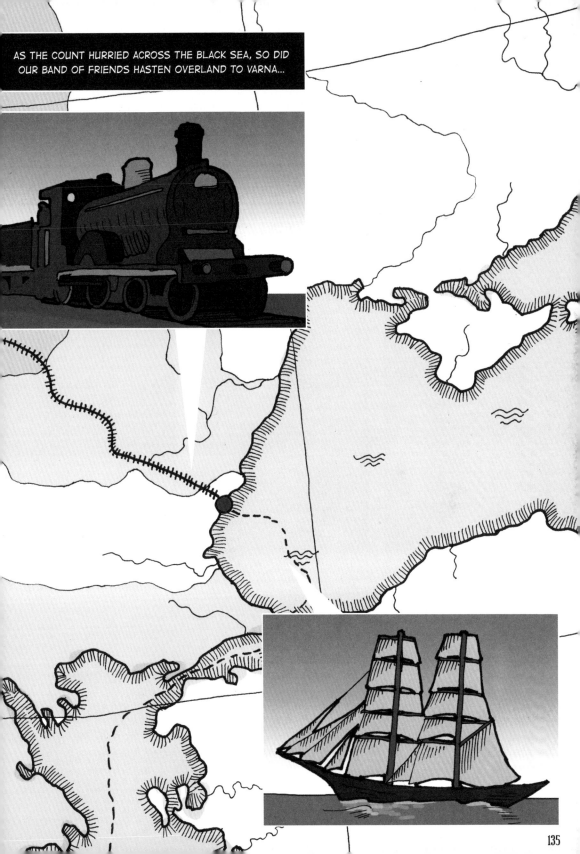

AS THE COUNT HURRIED ACROSS THE BLACK SEA, SO DID OUR BAND OF FRIENDS HASTEN OVERLAND TO VARNA...

THE *CZARINA CATHERINE* HAS BEEN DIVERTED--SHE HAS DOCKED AT GALATZ!

WHEN DOES THE NEXT TRAIN LEAVE?

6:30 TOMORROW MORNING!

HOW ON EARTH DO YOU KNOW?

I KNEW THAT IF ANYTHING WERE TO TAKE US TO CASTLE DRACULA WE SHOULD GO BY GALATZ, SO I MEMORIZED THE TIMES.

WONDERFUL WOMAN!

TOO KIND, PROFESSOR. NOW I MUST ARRANGE TICKETS FOR TOMORROW'S TRAIN.

Galatz

THE FOLLOWING MORNING THEY WENT TO INTERCEPT THE SHIP AT GALATZ.

IN ALL MY LIFE I'VE NEVER HAD SO FAVORABLE A RUN.

IT WAS AS THOUGH THE DEVIL HIMSELF WERE BLOWIN' ON OUR SAIL FOR HIS PURPOSE.

AND HAS ANY CARGO YET BEEN UNLOADED?

WHY YES. A MAN CAME ABOARD WITH AN ORDER TO RECEIVE A BOX MARKED FOR...

... OH--WHAT WAS HIS NAME...?

AH, YES, COUNT DRACULA.

AND THE NAME OF THE MAN WHO TOOK IT?

WHY SIR, PETROF SKINSKY. YOU MAY EVEN HAVE HIS ADDRESS!

Petrof Skinsky, Strada Tecuci 16

YOU'LL BE LUCKY. OLD SKINSKY'S DEAD. THEY JUST FOUND HIM IN THE CHURCHYARD!

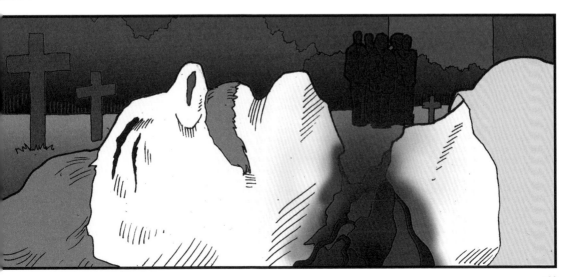

BACK AT THE HOTEL, THE GROUP GATHERED, DISPIRITED.

IT SEEMS WE FIND OURSELVES AT, QUITE LITERALLY, A DEAD END...

NOT NECESSARILY.

MY SURMISE IS THAT THE COUNT DECIDED TO CONTINUE BACK TO HIS CASTLE BY WATER, AS THE MOST SAFE AND SECRET WAY.

I HAVE EXAMINED THE MAP AND THERE ARE TWO MOST SUITABLE RIVERS FOR HIM TO ASCEND: THE PRUTH OR THE SERETH.

THE PRUTH IS MORE EASILY NAVIGATED, BUT THE SERETH RUNS UP AROUND THE BORGO PASS...

... FORMING A LOOP THAT TAKES IT VERY CLOSE INDEED TO CASTLE DRACULA!

MADAM MINA, YOUR EYES HAVE SEEN WHERE WE WERE BLINDED!

140

AND SO THEY SET OFF IN PURSUIT. ARTHUR HOLMWOOD AND JONATHAN HARKER BY STEAM BOAT...

... DR. SEWARD ON HORSEBACK...

... WHILE VAN HELSING AND MINA FOLLOWED BY TRAIN...

... THEN ONWARD BY CARRIAGE.

AT LAST, CASTLE DRACULA CAME INTO VIEW...

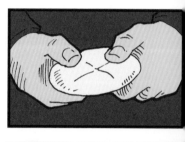

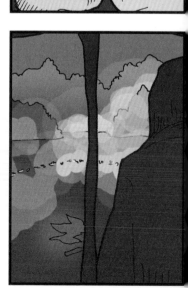

COME!

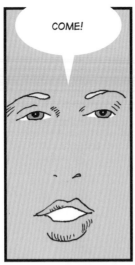

COME!

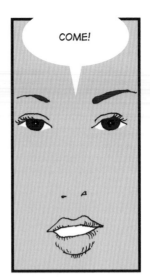

COME!

DEAR GOD!

HAHAHAHA

FOR THE REST OF THE NIGHT, MINA AND VAN HELSING REMAINED SAFE WITHIN THE SACRED RING.

A FATE NOT SHARED BY THE POOR HORSE, WHICH FELL VICTIM TO THE BRUTAL CHILL.

AS DAY BROKE...

SHE SLEEPS SOUNDLY AND WILL BE SAFE WITHIN THE CIRCLE OF HOLY HOST.

THERE ARE THINGS I MUST DO...

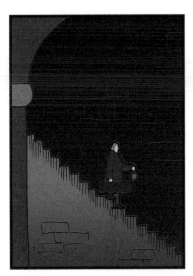

HE CAME UPON THE CHAPEL, WHERE COUNT DRACULA'S VAMPIRIC COVEN LAY AT REST.

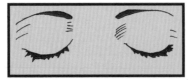

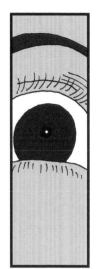

DRACULA

I BANISH YOU, UNDEAD, FROM THIS TOMB FOREVER!

151

THEY ARE ALL CONVERGING-- WE MUST BE PREPARED.

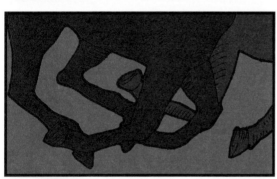

HALT!

THOSE RED EYES...

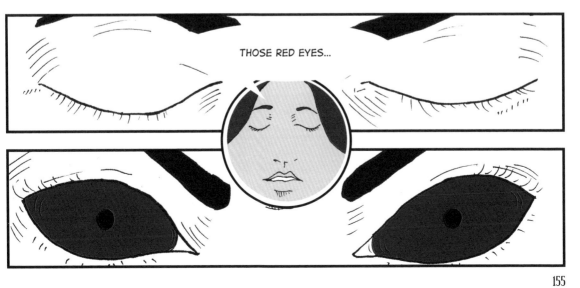

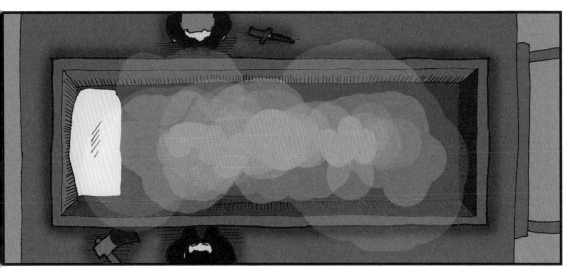

DEAR ARTHUR...

I AM ONLY TOO HAPPY TO BE OF SOME SERVICE TO YOU, DEAR MINA.

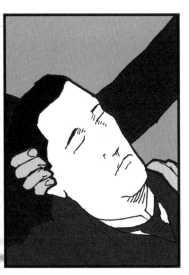

THE MARK HAS GONE FROM YOUR FOREHEAD. THE CURSE HAS PASSED AWAY!

AT LAST. WE ARE FREE.

Seven Years Later

HAVING CROSSED THE FLAMES, THE HAPPINESS OF MOST PLAYERS IN THIS ADVENTURE MEANT THE PAIN HAD BEEN WORTH ENDURING.

BOTH MINA AND JONATHAN SECRETLY BELIEVED THAT SOME OF ARTHUR'S BRAVE SPIRIT HAD PASSED INTO THEIR BOY, WHO BORE THE SAME NAME.

A RECENT TRIP BACK TO TRANSYLVANIA BROUGHT BACK MANY VIVID AND TERRIBLE MEMORIES AND THEY FOUND IT DIFFICULT TO BELIEVE THAT THE THINGS THEY HAD SEEN AND HEARD WERE LIVING TRUTHS.

CONVINCING ANYONE BEYOND THE TIGHT GROUP OF FRIENDS OF SUCH A WILD STORY WOULD THEREFORE BE IMPOSSIBLE.

BUT THAT WAS NOT THE POINT. AS VAN HELSING SAID TO YOUNG ARTHUR...

WE ASK NONE TO BELIEVE US! THIS BOY WILL ONE DAY KNOW WHAT A BRAVE AND GALLANT WOMAN HIS MOTHER IS.

ALREADY HE KNOWS HER SWEETNESS AND LOVING CARE. LATER ON HE WILL UNDERSTAND HOW SOME MEN SO LOVED HER, THAT THEY DID DARE MUCH FOR HER SAKE.

Acknowledgments

Matt Pagett would like to thank all at Quid Publishing, especially Lucy York whose patience and hard work made this book possible.